Reflections

My Three Year Journey to Freedom

Living with Multiple Sclerosis [MS]

Carolyn A. Legg
XO

First Edition, September, 2010

ISBN: 978-1-60643-602-8

Printed by Publisher Services [A division of Bar Code Graphics, Inc.]
875 N. Michigan Ave #2650
Chicago, IL 60611
312.595.0600 x240
312.664.0725 fax

Cover Photo and Book Design by Carolyn A. Legg

Paintings: Original Acrylic on canvas by Carolyn A. Legg

Cover Design by Donna Michitson, Kiwi Designs
781-662-4086
http://www.designsbykiwi.com/

God blesses the people who patiently endure testing.
Afterward they will receive the crown of life
that God has promised to those who love Him.

-- James 1:12 (NLT)
The Purpose Driven Life
by Rick Warren

Dedication

To Elaine, my heart and soul; thank you for your tireless support and love through all the trials and tribulations of "me/us" living with Multiple Sclerosis (MS) and always trying to understand what I go through; being there and helping me; even when I don't know I need it...You are loved!

Acknowledgements

I'd like to thank some very special people who in desperate times gave me strength to continue moving forward with my life.

From the bottom of my heart thank you mom and dad for loving me as I am. I love you very much!

Thank you to my family and friends (you know who you are!) for trying to understand what I go through on a daily basis. I love you!

A special thank you to Gail Spellman (Lahey Clinic, Burlington, MA) and May Bellisle (formerly of Lahey Clinic, Burlington, MA) for helping me through some of my hardest times dealing with MS...I definitely needed that iron fist wake up call! It sparked the fire in my heart again.

Thank you to Priscilla Griffin for your encouragement and affirmation in my writing abilities. It's through Priscilla's support this book finally came to be. Again to Priscilla and Nancy Parker for their time and effort helping edit my book. Then one day my computer up and crashed. Nancy currently had my only copy as she was doing a final edits (unbeknownst to me that she knew what happened) when she heard what happened, Nancy quietly retyped all my poems again, and there were a lot. When I received the book back she also handed me a disk and told me that she had retyped all the poems for me. I was taken aback by her selfless act of kindness and couldn't thank her enough. So Nancy, again thank you for all your wonderful work on my book!

Thank you to my dear friend, Roger Anderson, for taking time out of his busy schedule to sit with me and edit each poem...word for word. Your wisdom and insight has shed new light and made all the difference in my book and I am truly grateful for your support and more importantly your friendship!

Thank you to my dear cousin, Michelle Morgan, for taking the time to assist me in one of many rounds of edits – sometimes the right words make all the difference!

Thank you to my dear friend, Valerie Capone, for one last round of revisions. Though Val is quite the busy woman with her own writing, she gracefully took the time to read through my book for any last minute edits or corrections. I am deeply thankful to you Val for your wonderful friendship and talent as a writer. You are truly appreciated!

And finally, thank you to my wonderful and loving sister, Patrice, for taking the time out of her incredibly busy schedule for a final read through.

Dear Reader:

Multiple Sclerosis literally scooped me up from a life I was happy living.

I was attending college in the evening, with only two classes remaining to get my bachelors degree in computer information systems, while working full-time at a company for nearly 10 years, and then—Whoosh! In an instant, at the age of 40, I was displaced from school, from the work place, and from a life I was familiar living, being the person I had known myself to have always been. I attempted more than once to return to work, but it was taxing both physically and emotionally, and finally after two years of trying to keep the pace, my employer had to let me go. It was one of the hardest hits I would endure because I come from a background of hard workers who never gave up. I did not give up either, it was taken from me.

Multiple Sclerosis [MS] took its hold and I had absolutely no control over myself, my health, or my life.

I put up a fight, but the enormity of its reaches was beyond my physical and mental strength. I reluctantly gave in to its effects. What remained was despair and anger. The anger for losing what I had and who I thought I was. Now with my health's rapid decline seemingly out of nowhere, I was left with no answers and no remedies. I started to write about these feelings to help me cope, and to try to come to some resolve about it all.

Although I have been writing for over 25 years, I don't consider myself an expert or a scholar; but I've learned my being able to write about MS and my faith comes from a higher power, and that has allowed me to express and release my thoughts and emotions about this disease. I decided to share my story through a series of poems.

First, I share them for myself because of a driving need to express my feelings through writing. As you read on, I would like you to understand that they provide not only the chronology of my struggles with MS, but also a chronology of my faith and my acceptance of this disease.

Second, I want to share some of the effects of MS—not just the obvious clinical effects on the body that put a person in a wheelchair or on crutches, but its effects on the mind and spirit. If you have a loved one suffering from MS, it is my wish this book will help you better understand what some of us with this disease suffer on a daily basis and the lack of hope we can possess.

Third, the reason for sharing this collection is so that those of you who are challenged with MS will know you are not alone and that someone does understand and shares in your pain and anguish. As it may be with some of you, MS is one, if not the single hardest experience I will ever go through. However, having a loving family, supportive friends, and faith led me to this day, where I can share my poetry and artwork with you openly and honestly.

I cannot stress enough how underhanded a disease *Multiple Sclerosis* is.

How does one cope with it…more so, how would I?

Over the years I've come to learn being diagnosed with a chronic and often disabling disease would require a coping process not unlike that of the five-step grieving process when dealing with the loss of a loved one. Although the first stage of the process is *denial,* I omitted this stage in my collection because for the first 11 years after my diagnosis I was in denial, and it wasn't until I had a major exacerbation (attack by this disease on the myelin sheath [the protective coating covering the nerves] and leaving scar tissue damage) that these other stages could come to fruition.

This collection of poems focuses on *my own* experiences chronicling the sneak attack of MS and tracks a three year period following a major exacerbation.

For my specific purposes, the book is divided into four stages.

1. Bargaining
2. Anger
3. Despair
4. Acceptance

Perhaps my book will appear too raw, unedited, and at times angry. I realize those things, but the truth is all of those things. It is an account of my experiences since that first major attack.

Please also understand that some of my poetry contains strong imagery of the effects MS had on me *personally.* I write wholeheartedly of the anger and immense pain MS inflicted on me in immeasurable ways because it is often misinterpreted by doctors, the medical community, and many others—which for those of us suffering with it can be the most difficult part, as **MS is a hidden disease.** We may look fine on the outside, *but we are not* and the hidden pain affects all parts of a person: *heart, mind, body,* and *soul.*

With all this being said, know I have come to accept that throughout my life's journey, I will be permanently escorted by both Multiple Sclerosis and my faith in God. Without God, the journey with the first would be intolerable. I ask the reader to remember that I am describing *my own* pain and faith and that each of us must choose our own companion.

Wishing you peace and joy,

Carolyn A. Less

P.S. I have also included some clinical information at the end of the book, as well as MRI results of my brain. These images will show what a brain looks like with MS in comparison to a healthy brain. These pictures will shed more light into the destructive nature of this disease. It is also quite revealing to all that this is not an **external** *disease but an* **internal** *one.*

IV

Reflections

My Three Year Journey to Freedom

Living with Multiple Sclerosis [MS]

Contents

Introduction

My Three Year Journey to Freedom
Living with Multiple Sclerosis

Myelin Damage – MS Exacerbation

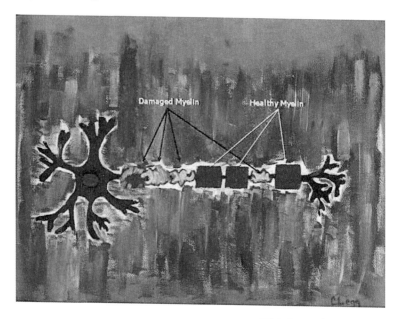

9"x12" Acrylic on Canvas

This is Me

I have a disease
The doctors tell me it's chronic
Called Multiple Sclerosis…

It was a secret
I was not to speak a word about
Just hide it away…

So…I did that
For a very long time
Kept it to myself…

So now it's gone
Locked deep inside me
But it is here…

Consuming my body
A little at a time
Only I know…

I look fine
It's difficult to see
But I feel it…

An every day struggle
To keep myself from defeat
I must be strong…

I pray now
To God I beg for His mercy
To keep me sane…

With His help
I am learning to accept this disease
It is part of me now…

Finally after so long, I'm okay
I know that I am still whole
This is me…

Part I – Bargaining

Definition: *To negotiate the terms of an agreement, as to sell or exchange; to engage in collective bargaining; to arrive at an agreement; to count on; expect.* With God it is called a "covenant" with MS there is no bargaining position.

We bargain or strike a deal with God, ourselves, or others to make the loss go away.

A Prayer for Healing

Dear God, so almighty
Creator of heaven and earth
Gracious and forgiving
Deliver unto me
My pain unto You…

Please Lord release me wholly
From this struggle I endure
And have mercy on me
Heal me with Your might
My body and mind completely…

Please take this from me
The suffering I concede to
Cleanse my body and soul
With a love only You can give
And purify me with Your will…

Please hear me speak
When I pray to You openly
How much I love You
How much I truly need You
You are my heart and soul…

I have never had the ability
To heal myself on the outside
Only You Lord, on the inside
Can truly heal my fears
Only You can make me whole again…

Please God make this be gone
A burden much too heavy
I no longer have the strength
To bear this pain in mortality
Heal me with Your glory…

Please Dear Lord
Give me back my strength
Allow me to re-connect
On the outside and in
Please Lord, make me well again…

Rescue Me

Rescue me from my tortured soul
 Let me know that I really am whole…

Please Lord free me from my hesitant views
 Give me strength to be able to choose…

Release the thoughts strangling what I need to find
 Let me know I can have peace of mind…

Rescue me from my deepest haunting fear
 Prove to me that You really do care…

Save me from what I did not know
 Show me I'm not the one who let go…

Abolish from me all my imminent pain
 Show me I can live again…

Rescue me from this haunting ache
 Tell me my faith is not a mistake…

Free me of the anguish my eyes do see
 Let me know my heart can be free…

Rescue me from the isolation of my time
 Let me know Lord I am Yours, You are mine…

Scream

11"x14" Acrylic on Canvas

The Truth

Dear Lord, please
I beg of Thee
Come to my aid
And rescue me...

I can no longer
Be defined by this
What MS has done
And all that I miss...

I am no longer certain
Who I was is gone
MS has taken me
Too far and too long...

To all the pain
And anguish inside
I can no longer fight
I can no longer hide...

My heart is barren
My soul is weak
My needs are rising
To the point I don't sleep...

What has become
Of the little girl inside
A piece of her soul
Has left and died...

For all this strain
Makes me angry and mad
The no longer having
Leaves me truly sad...

So again, dear Lord
I beg of Thee
Come to my aid
Please rescue me...

Forward-Backward

I take one step forward
Then two steps back
I realize this cliché
Is truth and fact...

I can no longer deny
The way I am today
Wishing my tomorrow
Was still my yesterday...

My future no longer bright
Stunted by my illness
As I pray to God
For love and His forgiveness...

It's difficult to move on
I'm not who I used to be
I fight hard to keep on going
Someday I hope I'll see...

Is this a gift to treasure?
Or the biggest mistake
That God has put upon me
To test my holy fate...

Today I still don't know
The lesson I am to learn
Without living in vain
Somehow I must discern...

So I'll take another step
Moving forward day by day
Hoping pain will be released
God by my side I'll be okay...

© 2009 Carolyn A. Legg 02-06-06

Humble Now

My life is very different now
From what it used to be
I realize I'm not the same
No longer the invincible me…

I'm not as sure as I thought
Is this how God shows His Love
To stop me in my tracks
His sign from heaven above…

I resist Him and think I'm strong
That I don't really need His aid
But somehow I know I'm wrong
I can't keep up this charade…

To let go and give all my will
Is so difficult for me to complete
But it's something I need to fulfill
With God I cannot compete…

This road a difficult passage
Not sure what will come about
But to refuse to hear His message
My soul will only hold doubt…

I see His glory in so many ways
Shining His light above so bright
And I know I cannot betray
Having faith in Him I know is right…

Rays of Hope II

9"x12" Acrylic on Canvas

Touched by an Angel

My worst fears have come to light
I am unable to continue
To go on...

Afraid and alone
Once again
I am on my own...

The pain and frustration
The anger and the helplessness
My feelings begin to overflow...

I am filled with self pity
Unable to be released
And...suddenly...

I awaken
Fall to my knees
And pray...

Asking for assistance
For help to show me the way
For a friend...

Someone came...stronger, more capable than I
Someone to speak with
Someone who really cares...

I am shown the way—But,
I fight hard
Still unable to understand...

Always the adversary, and
Slowly—Ever so slowly
I let go...

Releasing my doubts, I listen for once
And feel His words
I have become a believer...

Because I have been
Touched by an angel
And...I will never be the same...

Attack

9"x12" Acrylic on Canvas

My Torment

Paralyzed with its weight
I am doomed by unwanted fate
Of a disease I hate
For reasons you cannot debate...

Life as I have known it
Leaves me here to sit
Yearning for wit
But my mind has been hit...

It has been much too long
Once weak and then strong
What have I done wrong?
Again, I want to belong...

Make this just go astray
Please don't let it stay
I want to wake up one day
And this has all gone away...

Screaming prayers You don't hear
Are You really there?
Do You even care?
This torment that I bear?

When will Your time be right?
To help me win this fight
To free me from my plight
To give me back my might!

Just make it all go!
Free my body and soul
Of the passion MS stole
Because I am no longer whole!

The time is drawing near
It is the end that I fear
DO YOU EVEN CARE!
Where are You, Why aren't You here!

Please God, Save Me!!!

Part II – Anger

Definition: *A strong feeling of displeasure or hostility; a feeling of great annoyance or antagonism as the result of some real or supposed grievance; rage; wrath.*

We become angry with God, with ourselves or with others over our loss.

House of Blues

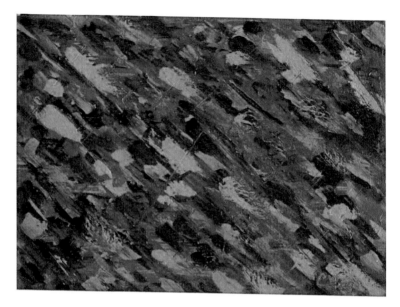

11"x14" Acrylic on Canvas

Funk

I'm in such a funk
My body turned to junk...
Can't get out of my own way
What a price to pay!

Melt Down

18x24 Acrylic on Canvas

Get Out!

To live with this disease
My mind has no ease
I'm turning inside out
I can only scream and shout...

Get Out!
Leave me be!
Let me go on!
With strength to be strong...

Get out now!
Leave my body somehow
Turn back time
To when I was in my prime...

Get out, now go
I just need to know
Please God give a sign
To my life be kind...

Just get the hell away
There's nothing more I can say
Because my prayers have ceased
Living with this disease...

No longer free to be
I finally see
I can no longer be alone
Or even on my own...

What a price to pay
When I no longer pray
Because He didn't hear
I wonder if He was ever there...

Now I am junk
Left in this body of funk
Just because of this disease
I no longer live with ease...

GET OUT!

Too Hot!

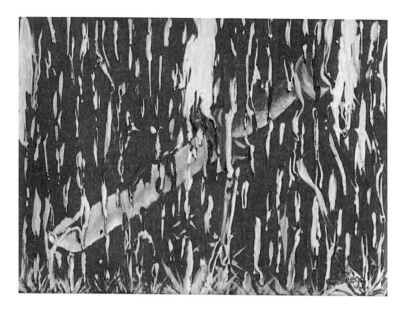

9"x12" Acrylic on Canvas

Too Hot!

The heat…Consumes me…

   Tiny beads of perspiration

      Trickling down my brow,

         Stinging my eyes,

            Turning my sight hazy…

               It's Too Damn Hot!

© 2009 Carolyn A. Legg 08-22-04

Organisms

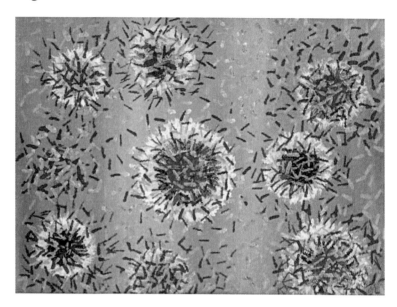

9"x12" Acrylic on Canvas

Creepy Crawlies

When the cycle does begin
Wrapping tight around my shin
It goes on more than a week
Making it too difficult to sleep...

I'm tired and I'm drained
Creepy crawlies won't abstain
My body's getting weak
And I find it hard to speak...

Restless are my legs
As I toss and turn all night
My mind is being sapped
This disease is now my trap...

Burning emanates all around
Sleep tonight cannot be found
The fire driving me insane
I just need to sleep again...

MS surely is not my friend...

Optic Neuro

16"x20" Acrylic on Canvas

Burden

I no longer want this burden
It weighs too heavy on my soul
Leaving me weak and abandoned
As scars begin to show…

There's a prisoner I see
Locked deep down inside
Oh My God, now I see
The prisoner outside is me…

I want the freedom that was mine
And I want it all back now
I want my life to rewind
Someway, somehow…

I want it all back now!

Patches

9"x12" Acrylic on Canvas Paper

Choices?

There are no choices
Left to be had
This is the way I am now
It leaves me bitterly sad…

For the life I once had
Is gone forever it seems
This is no longer a dream
But God's chosen scheme…

How do I contend?
With battles I'll face ahead
Knowing I'll never mend
To learn and live instead…

I'm afraid of this dread
Churning inside my soul
Where a piece of me is dead
Because I'm no longer whole…

"What is my goal?"
I ask God above
What do I need to do?
To prove my love to You…

I know my heart is true
Please Lord I ask of You
Come save this aimless soul
And heal my body through…

There's nothing more I can do
On my knees I'll pray to You
That You save this hopeless soul
And again make me whole…

Interference

9"x12" Acrylic on Canvas

Overload

It's all happening so fast
That I can no longer see
The edge of the forest
Where I can run and be free...

This disease that is here
Consuming my identity
Doesn't care why it's here
Or that it's my worst enemy...

How do I go on living?
This struggle every day
When I know You are not giving
The help I need as I pray...

It's too far ahead to see
And my mind is racing fast
As disease devours me
I wonder how long I will last...

I can't take this any longer
And I want You to know
I'm getting weaker not stronger
And it's beginning to show...

Where are You now
When I need You the most
To help me somehow
Rid this wicked ghost...

I'm so angry today
The tears refuse to flow
I don't know what to say
I'm on overload...

Rage

9"x12" Acrylic on Canvas

Contemptuous

This dreaded disease
Taking full control
Brings me to my knees
As it grasps my helpless soul...

I hate who I am
And what I have become
That tears no longer flow
My feelings are so numb...

Hurting and scornful
With a sneering glow
Disgusted by my life
And no where to go...

I pray to God in heaven
A continuous plea
I look to the sky above
But my soul continues to bleed...

I always feel the anger
And am dreadful of today
Damning my life
Because I'm not okay...

What will it take
To see my life through
If God refuses to help me
What else will I do?

I can't keep watching
As my body fades away
Discouraged by the future
Even as I pray...

So, what happens now
It's all up to You
Will You help me dear Lord
Help me make it through?

Part III – Despair

Definition: *To lose all hope; to be overcome by a sense of futility or defeat; the feeling that everything is wrong and nothing will turn out well.*

We become overwhelmed by the anguish, pain, and hurt of our loss; we are thrown into the depths of our sorrow.

Impact

This disease I have
Is very mysterious indeed
Strange things happen
All over my body...

They call it Multiple Sclerosis
A degenerative disease
There is currently no cure
And I fight hard to survive...

MS affects the brain
It also affects the spinal cord
Attacking the myelin sheath
Leaving damaging scar tissue...

Exposing these raw nerves
Fractures the smooth flow
Now these transmitters in my body
Leave me numb and rebellious...

I am unsuspecting
Innocent in the realization
Stopping me dead in my tracks
With an exacerbation of MS...

There are several medications
Each working to sustain
The amount of relapses occurring
But medication isn't a cure...

I am a warrior
I will fight this disease
As I pray to God for His strength
He's the one with the power...

Life Again

Sitting here in my office
On the computer I play games
Trying to figure out
How I get life back again...

The days are so long
The nights even longer
The will inside me is dying
I wish I was a little stronger...

Is it stress that makes the pain?
Or is it the pain that makes the stress?
I often wonder why
I was left with such a mess...

This disease now leaves me angry
And with such intense pain
I can't take this anymore
It causes too much strain...

All the prayers I prayed
Have left me in such sorrow
I'm waiting for the answer
Yet again, until tomorrow...

Where did I go wrong?
I cry to the Lord above
To carry this grief and woe
Why I'll never know...

So now I sit and wait
In dread and much despair
Will I ever be the same?
The answer is my biggest fear...

Confusion

18"x24" Acrylic on Canvas

My Fear

An epitaph
My realization of the now
Who I am and
What I have become...

A mixture of nothing
Aimless and resentful
Empty and hollow
Just water, molecules, and bones...

Endless days wandering
Into my own self loathing
Thoughts of devastation
Bubble over inside...

What the hell am I here for?
The question constantly nagging
My inner sanctum of peace
Shattered daily by reality...

My hopes and dreams
Quickly vanish before me
I stand here naked
Heart and soul barren...

What's left?
My fear of my own self
Knowing the never is here and
If I will ever be well again?

Relativity

Everything is relative
    In reality; in dreams…

I remember my dreams
    My subconscious haunts me now…

Bringing my disability
    To the forefront with ease…

Flowing back into consciousness
    And reality…

At last
    Acceptance?

MS Thoughts - Extremities

1.1

Toes curl and tense
Restless leg syndrome ensues
Devastating my body...

1.2

My body turns rigid
In an instant incinerates
My being to ashes...

1.3

Eyes distort - Immediately
Blurring perception and sight
All day and night...

1.4

Extremities burn deep
Alive and ravaging my body
The truth is surreal...

1.5

Extremities ablaze
Thriving on my defenseless body
Driving me insane...

Inner Toil

18x24 Acrylic on Canvas

Empty Now

This emptiness hides
Deep inside my soul
It's what I hold
Now leaving me cold...

I can't explain it
I wouldn't even try
The feelings inside
Bring a tear to my eye...

Too difficult to explain
Who I am today
Pain leaves me searching
For my yesterday...

All my truth
Is unclear to see
Rattling around my head
And blinding me...

No more asking why
I don't really care
Because even as I pray
My prayers You don't hear...

Have I lost all faith?
In my heart so deep
To the One I believe
The only truth I keep?

There are no answers
To me that are known
There are no signs left
To lead me home...

I just feel so alone...

Final Ruling

Well, the ruling is in
Now the time has come
Looking for a win
But this time it's done...

The prognosis at last
I wanted the doctor to lie
My heart beating fast
The results made me cry...

Lesions are not active
But I still have so much pain
Wanting to know the reasons
To be rid of constant strain...

Who I am now is what remains
Not who I used to be
There's no one left to blame
It is my destiny...

The road will be rough and long
But my heart will keep me true
His arms will hold me strong
My faith will get me through...

Save Me

I really wish I could be
Someone else other than me
The person that once cared
Is lost, alone, and scared…

I'm wriggling in my seat
Because constantly I am beat
Can't stand how I feel right now
I wish I could explain somehow…

My luck has definitely run out
In my head I shout
What can lie ahead?
Will my life change instead?

I've lost so much it seems
My life, my heart, and my dreams
What is left I could want?
Oh yes! Demons stop their taunt…

My mind and body are weak
So deep inside I cannot speak
My heart and soul are shown
Bleeding seeds I have sown…

Damage and heartache runs deep
Something inside I keep
But how to give in and let go
To Your grace I don't know…

My faith has been tested far
My soul shows deep, a scar
How can I really believe?
When I need Him most for reprieve…

No where can He be found
Can't feel Him near or around
I'm sinking deep and fast
Please God make this all my past…

Speak to me Lord so I can hear
And relieve me from my worst fear
Show me I'm someone who's dear
Because right now I need You here…

Release my pain so I can see
You love me just for me
Give me a sign that I am sane
Let me know my life's not in vain…

© 2009 Carolyn A. Legg 03-11-05/02-14-06

What Remains

18"x24" Acrylic on Canvas

My Destiny?

Tearing through my mind
MS clearly is not kind
And my body aches, so
Will it go, I just don't know?

This sad and bleak display
Of always feeling this way
And now my soul is lost
MS results at such cost...

This is such a big mistake
How much longer will it take?
Please God don't just let this be
My final chosen destiny...

For all the prayers I pray
Still the pain won't go away
A new relapse takes its toll
Another step back I now must go...

Eight months later I sit and cry
Don't want MS, I'd rather die
What good am I to sit at home?
To help no one I grieve alone...

Is my faith in God enough?
This battle alone is far too tough
I can no longer rid my pain
Please God help me live again...

Dear Lord, can You hear me now?
Please rescue me somehow
Oh, God make this go away
Please hear me, this I pray...

Please God hear me as I pray...

MS Daily Thoughts

Episode #1

Temperature rising quickly
Burning from the inside out
Ravishing my remains...

Episode #2

This Chronic Disease
An incurable, disabling endless struggle
I fight hard to overcome...

Acceptance

At times difficult
The reasons I was chosen
Trying to understand...

The Cure

To heal us
How long will it take!
Finding a cure...

Hectic

Thoughts running wild
Desperately searching for answers
Of what MS really is...

The Ride

I'm on this crazy ride
Of ups and downs of chronic
Fighting for my sanity...

Searching I

I search deep within
Looking for the strength to carry on
To find my Savoir...

Searching II

Searching my soul
For the inner strength
I know lies deep inside...

For God's Love

I am so dismayed
With decisions I have made
These thoughts leave me truly sad
And sometimes even mad...

I cannot see the light
God's hand is not in sight
The end is drawing near
In my heart I truly fear...

This place and how I am
No longer in my plan
Withering away in pain
God's faith in soul is slain...

Tender heart, I no longer feel
I wish a change, so I can heal
Now rehearsing all my prayers
Honesty bringing me to tears...

Fear soul's passion bare
I need for God to really care
Please give me a sign
With my mind and body, redefine...

Please God save this weary heart
I want to make a brand new start
For I have nothing left to give
And this is no way to live...

Send a sign for You to show
How You truly love me so
Please God heal me with Your powers
Full grown petals of Your flowers...

That will spring me back to life
With love in heart no longer strife
And when I feel You inside my soul
Then, and only then will I be whole...

Battle to Freedom

9"x12" Acrylic on Canvas

Battle to Freedom

Incessant fatigue
Brings me to my knees
Every day and night
This struggle – my fight...

The MS just won't go
As stress begins to show
I am at my final end
With no idea how to mend...

I was so viable before
But MS took that for sure
It's been over two years
Still living with these fears...

This life I now have
Makes me angry and sad
I shout and I scream
Is this a bad dream?

I can never go back
The before which I lack
No feelings of glee
Now my soul bleeds...

If I could turn back time
To the life that once was mine
I'd be different you'd see
I'd be free to be the old me...

Heart and Soul

There are too many sleepless nights
Always filled with wracking pleas
As I beg for some of your solace
Crawling from my bed onto my knees...

I am horrified by the reality
Of my disenchanting dreams
I finally lose my burning battle
Opening my ears to hear my screams...

I am always hoping and I pray
For the early morning light
How very close I know I am
To losing my deepest, darkest fight...

My nightmares they persist
I can't feel you any more
As I search for heavenly bliss
Still I try but I'm never sure...

Please come to me, my rescue
I want the safety of Your soul
I need Your strength to keep me true
Your wisdom and grace to make me whole...

Frailty

I'm teetering on the edge
Of living life incomplete
Looking over the ledge
Knowing I can't compete…

No longer feeling whole
This gaping wound does seep
Deep into my soul
Where pain is what I keep…

I deny the true reality
Of who I am today
Strength has turned to frailty
Leaving me hopeless as I pray…

No guidance to be had
I don't know what to do
These feelings leave me sad
Because I really do need You…

I want a second chance
To live a life that's filled
With songs to make me dance
Please give me one more chance…

© 2009 Carolyn A. Legg 03-13-06

46

Lesions

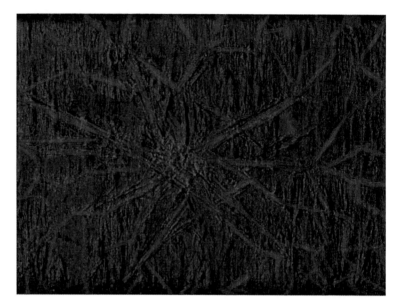

11"x14" Acrylic on Canvas

Lesions

I am not prepared
As they consume by mind
I am just not ready…

Just in Time

Take this feeling
From my soul
Before it's too late
Before I must go...

Help me believe
That You are here
That I'm not for nothing
That You really do care...

Take my heart
Believe in it still
With all that is in me
You have all my will...

And with my soul
Rise high and above
My turmoil and pain
To bring peace again...

MS Thoughts

Symptoms

Symptoms are real
Not an illusion
I am sane...

Heat

Body temperature rising
I'm ready to self-destruct
From the inside out...

Living Hell

This is living hell
And I see no way
To be free...

Part IV – Acceptance

Definition: *The mental attitude that something is believable and should be accepted as true; complex mental state involving beliefs, feelings, values, and dispositions to act in certain ways.*

We begin to reach a level of awareness and understanding of the nature of our loss.

The Whole Truth

A dark blue couch
As well as my bed
Or pacing my condo
With an aching head...

My mind always railing
As I question why
I have this disease
That makes me cry...

Because of the unknown
MS does cause
With fear I hide
In a breathless pause...

On the surface you say
I look just fine
But on the inside of me
To see, you are blind...

There are many degrees
Of symptoms that cause
This dreaded disease
Please stop and pause...

With the kindest of heart
Bear with me my friend
For I must live with
MS till the end...

There is no cure
How frightful indeed
Like a ticking time bomb
Exploding its seed...

Into symptoms that reduce
What I am capable to do
Turning me inside out
And away from you...

So that you can't see
What I have become
My life at a standstill
Turning me numb...

And shriveling me up
To feel small and meek
MS is a struggle
Now turning me weak...

It's too difficult to tell
How can I explain?
The symptoms are real
With MS comes pain...

But I want you to know
Please don't pity me
For this is my life
Planned by God you see...

I want to tell the world
So everyone can hear
I have this disease
That I'd like to bear...

All I ask
Is that you stop to learn
About this disease
With great concern...

Because all too many
Are diagnosed each day
And they are in the dark
They are not okay...

Let's bridge this gap
Information is key
To learn about MS
Please join me...

You might surf the web
Or you could buy a book
To learn of this disease
You should take a look...

Because MS is cruel
And it affects all kinds
Taking our mobility
As well as our minds...

This is my reality
My whole truth to show
How MS makes me feel
That I want you to know...

The History of My Disease

It's been a long time
Since I had to face the reality
Of living with this chronic disease...

When I finally learned of it
I was shocked and dismayed
Fear began to consume me...

I was 27 years old then
No insurance coverage for the medication
I only felt fear and frustration...

When I thought I was relapsing
The doctor I would see about my MS
Would look at me like I was over-reacting...

He said I should wait
It's got to go on for more than 3 days
Only then I should call him and he'll help...

The arrogance of this doctor
The pompous nature of all the doctors
Drove me away and on my own...

This led me to my prayers
With the guidance of God in my heart
He took it from me for a while...

With full time work and endless night school
Running me ragged
Indicators began to emerge...

Now, 11 years later
I have begun to see the light
Things were never what they seemed...

My body started to give out
Fatigue began its course
But really...It started a long time ago...

I never knew what the signs were
And the doctors would never listen
Figuring it's all in my head...

Shielding myself from this disease
I chose to escape it and tried to forget
Didn't bother to learn about it...

Little by little it started
Symptoms were creeping up on me
Slowly disintegrating my senses...

Now...Difficult to grasp
My fleeting focus and
Lack of ability to concentrate...

Things that were second nature
Are now difficult to maintain
My brain has myelin damage...

Body parts ache regularly
I often wonder where it comes from
Curious about the lesions...

I need to know more about MS
If I don't know my own disease
Who will really help me?

I have struggled for months
These active lesions on my brain
Tearing me down bit by bit...

I can no longer run away
Accepting may be the easy part
But it is the hardest thing to do...

Again, I look to God and pray
Longing for His guidance and direction
I can feel Him with me...

There's a reason He chose me
Something I can do - with Him in my heart
I can overcome anything...

I have chosen to accept my reality
And maybe I can help someone else
If it's only one person, well then, that's okay...

God's Love [1]

I awaken
No longer a stranger
To embrace
His unclaimed love…

Resurrected anew
Finally
I am whole
With God…

I Am Found[2]

His face descended
My eyes of tears
And sorrow slowly drifted...

No longer alone
God's love
Realized...

And
I am finally
Found...

[2] Ibid

Into the Light

11"x14" Acrylic on Canvas

His Dare [3]

Gazing up...

Night gathered endless space...

A higher power called...

Daring me...

To love life greater...

[3] Ibid

Night Life

Late at night
The words flow easily
I write steady…

A story emerges
Sometimes rhyme, sometimes prose
It doesn't matter…

Faith guides me
And the meaning is clear
I become whole…

The words written
Of whom I have become
Give me peace…

With God's guidance
I have the ability to express
All that I desire…

I am finally whole
Having faith in His love
My life is truth through Him…

The Lord's Love [4]

Tears stood still
With my heart aching
I gazed upon a cloud…

And
The Lord's love
I found…

I cried…

[4] Ibid

Taking Flight

9"x12" Acrylic on Canvas

Reborn [5]

Innocence captured
Falling crippled
To demons alive…

A dream borne
Of angel wings
Peacefully glowing…

I found
My answer in
Love of God…

---

[5] Ibid

My Tomorrow

My eyes mingle
With misty waters
A silver horizon...

Dreams surfaced and
Drifted in shadows
Of tomorrow...

A new day...

I Am

Everything with His glory
When I open my heart
A true believer…

Possibilities are endless
Trusting in His splendor
I am who He is…

Empty when I stray
A mere mortal in reality
I am a stranger in His house…

In my heart I now know
After wandering aimlessly for years
I am not alone…

He is here to guide me
When I give myself all to Him
I am finally whole…

Re-Birth

11"x14" Acrylic on Canvas

Awakening

Restless am I
Now awake in my bed
Longing for sleep…

Focus is off
Double vision is my sight
Faulty images result…

Mumbled thoughts ensue
To concentrate a difficult task
Eager for clarity…

Body is flaccid
Losing control of my limbs
Damaged myelin attacks…

Speech is slurred
Face and mouth are numb
Inebriated with disease…

Body parts ache
On the outside and in
A deteriorating disease…

Far too long
Running from my disease now
Slapping my face…

Revealing myself wholly
Knowing what I have become
Accepting my reality…

No longer resisting
His challenge to fight accepted
My gift now…

Celebration

9"x12" Acrylic on Canvas

What Do You See

What do you see
When you look at me?
Am I still the person
I used to be?

Or do you see disease
Taking over me?
In my head, my heart
Almost all of me…

Can you see the pain
I learned to hide so well?
Or feel the feelings
I seldom tell?

Can you understand the anguish
That threatens my soul?
Or understand the reasons
I am no longer whole?

Can you try to comprehend
How MS takes its toll?
Affecting my entire body
Where I lose control…

I don't have any answers
But please realize
This disease that binds me
Is not a disguise…

MS made me different
I struggle each day
But I'm much better you see
Because…Finally I'm free!

From Beyond [6]

I breathe in
Slowly
The chants of prayer...

And comfort comes
In words
Whispering softly...

I listen intently
From beyond as
His love calls...

[6] Ibid

My Hope [7]

Paint brushed softly...

Desire of hope
Washed dry...

Prayer found Him...

And my soul
Became my paintings...

© 2009 Carolyn A. Legg 04-14-05

My Dedication

A light that shines
Brings peace in knowing
You are who I am…

Life as a writer
And an artist
Is peaceful…

My work here is
And always will be
A dedication to You…

Without You

A lost soul
Wondering aimlessly
Into nothingness...

I am not complete
Without You by my side
To guide me...

My life is not content
If You are not in my thoughts
To bring me peace...

My restless heart
Searches deep inside
And discovers You...

Alas! I finally see
Life has no meaning
Without You!

Final Note

MS is a world in and of itself.

The degree of *disabling* and *non-disabling* symptoms to be considered are immeasurable; so many tests need to be taken to conclude this disease...MRIs, evoked potential tests (this test measured the time it took for my brain to process the sensation); then once through those tests I went for an eye test, hearing test, and the usual mobility/balance, pin-prick for sensation, etc.

So many lives it has and will affect. Still today, after all the research and discovery, some doctors still think/feel MS does not cause pain (this fact is based on my personal experiences with MS doctors less than three years ago). For obvious reasons it can be misunderstood...pain *can't* be seen.

There is no cure for this disease, but with each and every penny donated to the National Multiple Sclerosis Society, they can, have, and will continue to help those suffering. We need your support to find the cause and the cure.

My heart and prayers go out to those who have been affected by MS and the countless others who are affected by this hideous disease through experience or through loved ones.

In closing, I share a final poem with you on how others have reacted to my *physically invisible* symptoms that affect me personally.

Presumptuous

How dare you look at me
With questionable doubt
As I speak of my disease
You know nothing about…

I may look just fine
But on the inside of me
Damage wreaks havoc
That you'll *never* see…

And why I care
That you have the facts
Is to avoid embarrassment
And verbal attacks…

Because if I walk okay
But use my handicap plate
You look at me
With aversion or hate…

I cannot keep explaining
Because you haven't a clue
How MS *affects me*
And what *I* live through…

But…I always feel a need
To explain or defend
What people don't know
Of a disease with no end…

All I ask of you
Is to *please* keep in mind
You know nothing of me
So please try to be kind…

What is Multiple Sclerosis? [8]

MS is thought to be an auto-immune disease that affects the central nervous system (CNS). The CNS consists of he brain, spinal cord, and the optic nerves. Surrounding and protecting the nerve fibers of the CNS is a fatty tissue called myelin, which helps nerve fibers conduct electrical impulses.

In MS, myelin (please refer to Myelin Damage – MS Exacerbation on page 8) is lost in multiple areas, leaving scar tissue called sclerosis. These damaged areas are also known as plaques or lesions. Sometimes the nerve fiber itself is damaged or broken.

Myelin not only protects nerve fibers, but makes their job possible. When myelin or the nerve fiber is destroyed or damaged, the ability of the nerves to conduct electrical impulses to and from the brain is disrupted, and this produces the various symptoms of MS.

[8] http://www.nationalmssociety.org

Who Gets MS? [9]

- Anyone may develop MS, but there are some patterns.
- Most people with MS are diagnosed between the ages of 20 and 50.
- *Twice* as many *women* as men have MS.
- Studies indicate that genetic factors make certain individuals more susceptible than others, but there is no evidence that MS is directly inherited. (*I have an older second cousin on my mother's side that was diagnosed years before me and a first cousin on my father's side diagnosed years after me. I grew up on the North Shore in Massachusetts as did my second cousin, however my first cousin grew up on the South Shore in Massachusetts.*)
- MS occurs more commonly among people with northern European ancestry, but people of African, Asian, and Hispanic ethnicity are not immune.
- Approximately 400,000 Americans acknowledge having MS, and *every week about 200 people are diagnosed.* Worldwide, MS may affect 2.5 million individuals.

[9] http://www.nationalmssociety.org

Symptoms of Multiple Sclerosis [10]

Symptoms of MS are unpredictable and vary from person to person and from time to time in the same person. For example, one person may experience abnormal fatigue, while another might have severe vision problems. A person with MS could have loss of balance and muscle coordination making walking difficult; another person with MS could have slurred speech, tremors, stiffness, and bladder problems. While some symptoms will come and go over the course of the disease, others may be more lasting.

Most Common Symptoms

- Bladder Dysfunction *
- Bowel Dysfunction *
- Changes in Cognitive Function, including problems with memory, attention, and problem-solving *
- Dizziness and Vertigo *
- Depression and other Emotional Changes *
- Fatigue (also called MS lassitude) *
- Difficulty in Walking and/or Balance or Coordination Problems *
- Abnormal Sensations such as Numbness or "pins and needles" *
- Pain *
- Sexual Dysfunction
- Spasticity *
- Vision Problems, Optic Neuritis *

Less Common Symptoms

- Headache *
- Hearing Loss *
- Itching *
- Seizures
- Speech and Swallowing Disorders *
- Tremors *

* Effects of MS on me personally

---

[10] http://www.nationalmssociety.org

MRI Results

Healthy Brain vs. Myelin Damage (Lesions/Plaque) on My Brain

Healthy Brain

(www.dkfz-heidelberg.de/.../tflt103.html)

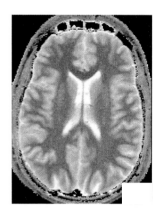

My MRI Scans at Lahey Clinic, Burlington, MA

April 12, **2003**

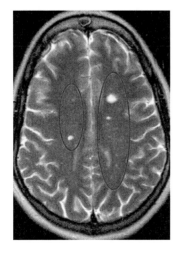

April 10, **2007**

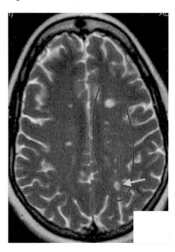

Damage is indicated by the white circle-like matter.

New Lesions appear in the 2007 MRI scan indicated by yellow arrow.

White lesions may or may not heal where black lesions are permanent damage.

MRI Results

Healthy Brain vs. Myelin Damage (Lesions/Plaque) on My Brain

Healthy Brain

http://www.health.com/health/static/hw/media/m
edical/hw/h9991221.jpg

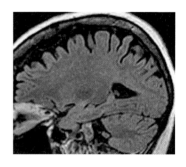

My MRI Scans at Lahey Clinic, Burlington, MA

April 12, **2003**   April 10, **2007**

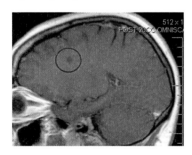   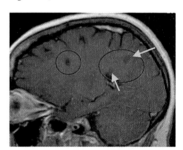

Damage is indicated by the black circle-like matter.

New Lesions appear in the 2007 MRI scan indicated by yellow arrow.

White lesions may or may not heal where black lesions are permanent damage.

Credits

Thank you to the National Multiple Sclerosis Society website for their information on:

- What is Multiple Sclerosis?
- Who Gets MS?
- What Are the Symptoms?

For additional information, please go to: http://www.nationalmssociety.org

Poets.com

Poetry in Motion is a daily contest I entered when I was a member of Poets.com. A sample of the format is below. Each day I would log on and arrange the words, and then I would write a poem of 20 tiles or less and submit.

Layout of scrambled words

After Arranging

I then arrange the words to complete a 20 tile poem and click submit

In Closing

People asked me why I felt it necessary to write this book and my answer was quite simple. I needed to write this book about my struggles with MS and living through its affects. It has helped me re-gain my faith and taught me that despite the circumstances I am alive and well. Even when some days aren't so good, I also know that there will *always* be days that are — so I take advantage of those days and pray for strength the other days.

I finally realized that MS does not define who or what I am. It is just another part of my life that I now embrace and am intensely grateful for, as crazy as that sounds. You see if it were not for being diagnosed with MS and having a major exacerbation, I would not have found my voice through writing this book or creating my paintings. All I know is I received a gift from God, and we all know how gifts may be perceived when one cannot see the light. But when I was able to finally *see*, it all became clear.

So with this gift—and faith—I have become a survivor and for that I am truly blessed.

Thank you for purchasing my first poetry series focused on living with Multiple Sclerosis. I hope you enjoyed the poems and were able to gain insight as I wrote about my journey with MS from diagnosis to progression on a daily basis.

Please look for *Reflections, Series II* coming soon.

If you would like further information or to discuss anything you have read, please feel free to contact me at <u>samsbuddie@yahoo.com</u>. Additionally, if you are interested in purchasing a painting, they will be for sale at a later date. There will also be a limited number of signed and numbered lithographs of each painting in this series.